The Beezer Book

Printed and Published by D. C. THOMSON & Co., Ltd., Dundee and London.

TROUBLE ALL THE WAY—A REAL CAT-ASTROPHE!

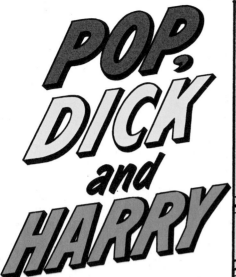

WHAT A CARRY ON!

The kangaroo of Australia has a large pouch in which it carries its young. Even after the young kangaroo can run and jump, it still climbs into the pouch for shelter.

The main food of the furry koala bear is the leaves of the eucalyptus tree. As the koala climbs through the branches, the baby bear clings to its mother's back.

Young hippos believe in taking things easy. When their mother goes for a swim, they steal a ride on her back.

Until they are well able to protect themselves, tiger cubs seldom stray far from their mother's side. When the tiger makes its way through the jungle, it carries its young in its powerful jaws.

The American opossum has a long, curved tail which it can curl round branches as it moves through the trees. Sometimes, a baby opossum will curl its tail round its mother's, to be carried about.

As the ant-eater of South America searches for ants and termites, the baby ant-eater balances on its mother's back.

THAT NIGHT.

WHAT KIND OF DRINK IS THIS? I'VE NEVER SEEN IT BEFORE.

IT'S NOT TEA, AND IT ISN'T COFFEE.

MOUTH DEPT.

I'LL TAKE SOME UP TO BRAINY. HE MIGHT BE ABLE TO TELL US WHAT IT IS— OOPS! IT'S HOT!

NOW, WHAT COULD BE JAMMING THAT SWITCH?

BRAINY, WHAT IS...OOPS!

TRIP!

TOOLS

WAH! THAT'S HOT!

THUD!

LIGHT SWITCH

ON

OFF

OUCH!

LIGHT SWITCH

ON

CREAK!

CLICK!

OFF

HURRAH! THE LIGHTS ARE OUT! NOW WE CAN ALL GET TO SLEEP.

SNORE!

I SLEPT LIKE A LOG, THANKS TO THIS STUFF! WONDER HOW IT WORKS?

SNOOZO

Black Bun

FINGERS OF THE BADD LADS

MR FLIPPY

MR FLIPPY was a spaceman who was stranded on Earth when his rocket ship ran out of fuel. While searching for the special fuel he needed to return to his far-off planet home, he was befriended by Billy Gray and his Mum and Dad, and they invited the spaceman to stay with them.

WE'LL SOON BE FINISHED AT THIS RATE.

Billy Gray and Mr Flippy had been given the job of putting up the Christmas decorations. It was easy for the spaceman—he could use his sucker feet to walk up the walls!

HI, DAD! BUT WHERE'S THE TREE?

But, with a clever spaceman around the house, there was no need to despair!

I'LL GET YOU A TREE!

Mr Flippy made a bee-line for the nearby estate, where there were fir trees galore. But the ground was frozen hard. A spade was no good.

PHEW! THE GROUND'S LIKE CONCRETE.

Whoosh! Suddenly the tree popped out of the ground, roots and all!

OOF!

Poor Mr Flippy was so startled by the suddenness that he gasped — and lost all his puff! Down he crashed like a ton of bricks, with the tree on top of him. And more trouble was on the way—a nosey gamekeeper!

OUCH!

HELLO, LADS! I'VE GOT THE REST OF THE CHRISTMAS PRESENTS.

Dad hadn't brought the most important purchase of all.

THE SHOPS ARE SOLD OUT, BILLY! WE'LL HAVE TO DO WITHOUT.

So Mr Flippy performed another of his unusual feats. Pinching his nose, he inflated himself and floated aloft like a balloon.

Grabbing the top of the selected tree, the spaceman puffed himself up bigger and bigger . . .

HO! WHAT'S GOING ON HERE?

The spaceman lost no time in grabbing the tree and skedaddling straight up the wall. The gamekeeper aimed.

STOP—OR I'LL FIRE!

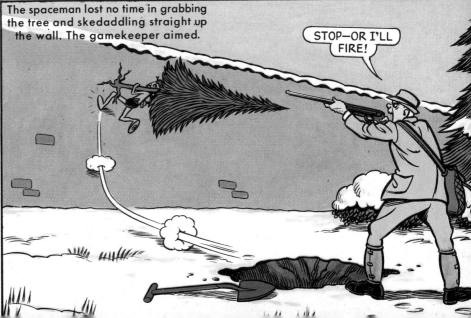

As Mr Flippy hopped off, the startled gamekeeper yelled in terror as the ground around the hole suddenly collapsed. Down into the murky depths he plunged.

Unaware of the gamekeeper's fate, Mr Flippy pressed on homewards. But so great was his haste that he took a wrong turning. In two ticks he was lost. And when he did come to a signpost, it was thick with snow.

The spaceman looked over the wall to see who had shouted. There were only two snowmen there and they couldn't have shouted. However, there were two sledges . . .

Mr Flippy decided to borrow them to transport the tree. And that's when funny things began to happen.

The schoolboys' sledges were smashed to bits. This was the wrong moment to apologise, Mr Flippy reckoned, so he took to his heels.

The spaceman came to a bus stop. Taking a bus might be the safest and quickest way home.

Without more ado, Mr Flippy boarded the first bus, carrying the tree over his shoulder.

HOOLIGAN!

Poor Mr Flippy and his tree got the heave in double-quick time. That was the shortest bus trip he'd ever taken!

The furious passengers descended upon the tree and grabbed their parcels. The tree was ripped.

WE WANT OUR PARCELS!

But there's lots a spaceman can do—especially with a gun that can make things grow!

SILLY ASS! LOOK WHAT YOU'VE DONE!

GOLLY!

Mr Flippy fired the gun at the tree and it grew and grew—and didn't stop till it had crashed through the ceiling! The Grays raised the roof at that!

Through the bus, the spaceman marched, looking for a seat. All he found was loads of trouble as the branches of the tree whipped parcels out of the passengers' hands.

HOI!

GET HIM OFF THIS BUS!

HOI!

Woefully, Mr Flippy surveyed the ruin.

GOSH!

Home he plodded with the six-inch top of the tree. Billy was dismayed.

WHAT HAPPENED?

I—ER—HAD AN ACCIDENT!

Back at the estate, the dazed gamekeeper was slowly regaining his senses. The poor man had fallen into a secret tunnel. But where did it lead?

The gamekeeper decided to find out —and not a couple of yards away, he spotted a big, old chest. What was inside took his breath away.

Meanwhile, inside the big house on the estate, Squire Squiggle was about to have dinner. Nebby, his faithful retainer, served the festive fare— sausages!

YOUR SAUSAGES. SIR!

AGAIN?

Squire Squiggle was delighted. The family fortune which had been lost for hundreds of years, had come to light again! What a difference this would make to his life! Why, he could have Christmas cake every day of the year!

I FOUND THE SECRET TUNNEL WHILE CHASING THAT MR FLIPPY FELLOW.

So along to the big house everyone trooped to tuck into the biggest Christmas dinner ever. And Mr Flippy didn't forget about the lads whose sledges he'd broken. He asked the Squire to buy new ones for them. What a marvellous time everyone had!

MERRY CHRISTMAS!

THE LAUGHS ARE GOOD WITH FLYING FOOD!

SILLY CHUMP! IT WASN'T THE BUMP!

COLONEL BLINK
THE SHORT-SIGHTED GINK

CRAZY CAPERS

Sailors have gone to sea in all kinds of strange craft —but an American once sailed from Florida to New York in a boat made from old newspapers!

As if bullfighting wasn't dangerous enough, a famous Mexican matador once fought a bull while riding a bicycle!

Long ago, anyone challenged to a duel had the right to choose the weapons. But one duellist got a shock when his Hungarian opponent chose— cannons!

Safe-snatching was too tame for a thief who broke into Sanger's Circus. He headed for the animal cages—and stole a lion!

How's this for a hair-raising stunt! A French actor had such powerful hair "muscles" he could make his hair stand on end or curl in any direction.

A Rumanian had so much electricity in his body he could turn himself into a human torch! All he had to do was fasten a wire to his body then connect the other end to a bulb.

Talk about "high" tea! The famous high-wire walker, Blondin, once cooked an omelette while balancing on a rope stretched across the Niagara Falls. To make the stunt more dangerous, he wheeled the stove across in a barrow!

A Florida man had a narrow escape when a big circular saw suddenly crashed through his house wall, sliced his breakfast table in two, then hurtled on through the opposite wall! The huge blade had broken free from a sawmill next door.

"...DIGGING A TUNNEL AND TAKING MULLIGAN BY SURPRISE?...

"...SHOULD I CHALLENGE MULLIGAN TO SINGLE COMBAT AND FORCE HIM TO SURRENDER? THAT MIGHT BE EXCITING...

"...OR SHOULD CAP'N BRAINY LEAP AT HIS FOE AND TIE HIM IN KNOTS AFTER A STRENGTH-SAPPING STRUGGLE?"

HEY, BRAINY! HERE COMES MULLIGAN AND HIS MOB.

NOW'S YOUR CHANCE TO GET THE ENDING FOR YOUR STORY. GET OUT THERE AND DEAL WITH MULLIGAN, THEN WRITE DOWN WHAT YOU REALLY DO!

GOSH! HE'S NOT USUALLY SO KEEN TO GET AT MULLIGAN.

GRR! BRAINY MUST'VE SEEN ME COMIN'! LOOK AT HIM GO.

HAW! HAW! HAW! BRAINY'S GOT THE ENDING TO HIS STORY—'THE BRAVE CAP'N BRAINY TURNED TAIL AND FLED'. HO! HO! HO!

MY, OH MY—WHAT A FUNNY PIE!

5 MINUTES LATER...

GOSH! IT'S FINISHED ALREADY! I'D BETTER MAKE ANOTHER ONE BEFORE MUM COMES BACK!

NOW LET'S SEE WHAT'S IN THE LARDER. MUM SAID SHE USED UP BITS AND PIECES.

...ONE OLD SAUSAGE...

...TWO COLD POTATOES...

OOH, YES...SOME SAUCE...

TAP! TAP!

...A HANDFUL OF PRUNES AND A TIN OF SPAGHETTI!

NOW, I'LL PUT THE CRUST ON AND POP IT INTO THE OVEN!

LATER—

NO TIME FOR DINNER, MUM! I'M OFF TO THE FOOTBALL MATCH!

CRUMBS! I DON'T LIKE THE LOOK OF THAT!

ALL THE MORE FOR US, SMIFFY!

I WAS AFRAID YOU'D SAY THAT!

GROOH! IT'S AWFUL!

HOW DARE YOU SAY THAT ABOUT MY PIE!

WHACK!

CROOKED SMILES

FUN GALORE ON THE SHORE!

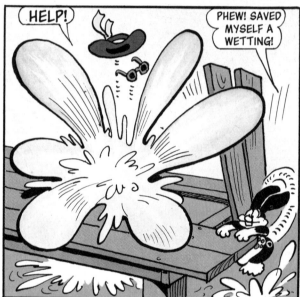

COLONEL BLINK

THE SHORTSIGHTED GINK

Old Ben
THE BADGER

HIGH in the hills above Glen Arlee lives Old Ben, the badger. For years he has hunted there and battled against wildcats, foxes and eagles. Ben has survived because he's tough—and wily.

[on]e hot summer day, Ben stuck his snout cautiously out [of h]is sett. He was hungry—and he knew just where to find a nice juicy snack.

[Bu]t,as he ambled across a clearing,Ben heard an angry hiss—it was Varga the wildcat.

The old badger caught a fleeting glimpse of deadly yellow fangs and bared claws streaking towards him.

Ben instinctively reared up, parried the killer blow, and with a lightning swipe of his paw, sent his opponent spinning.

Then he braced himself for another attack. But Varga had had enough. With an angry, backward glance, the wildcat beat a retreat.

Ben hurried on through the undergrowth till he came to a clearing. Just beyond the trees was a cottage, and in the garden grew strawberries—Ben's favourite food on a hot summer's day. But Ben wasn't the only one who knew about the titbits in Dave Newby's garden.

Just as Ben reached the clearing, a family of roe deer leaped over the fence into the garden.

The fawn was fascinated by the bright red berries. So, while his mother and father were contentedly munching the cabbages, he squirmed under the net on the strawberry patch.

By the time Ben arrived, the fawn was well and truly trapped under the net.

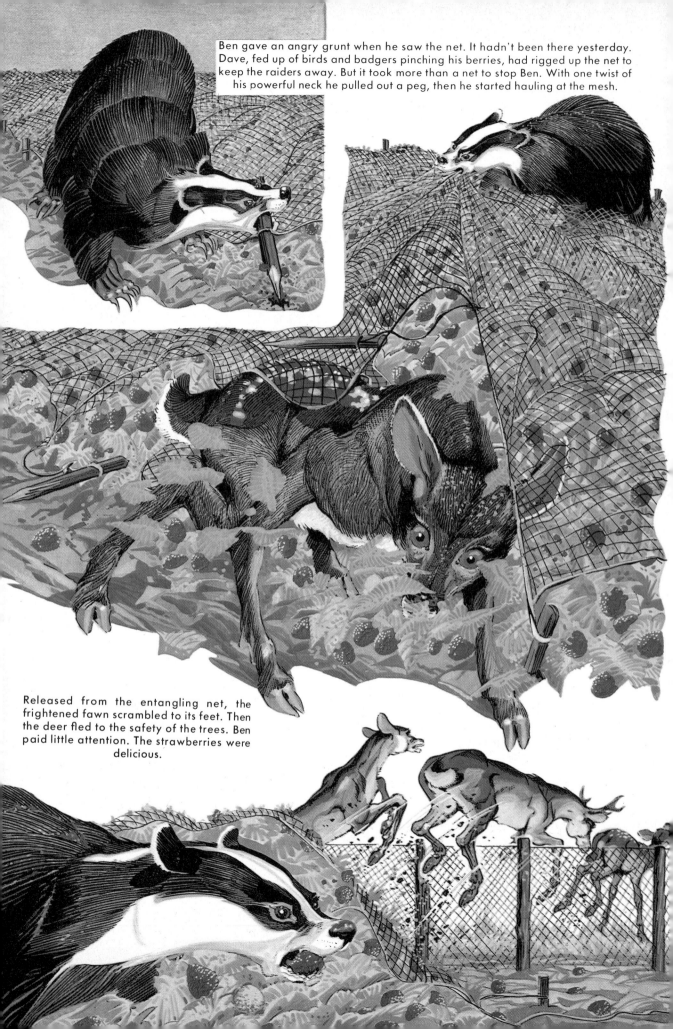

Ben gave an angry grunt when he saw the net. It hadn't been there yesterday. Dave, fed up of birds and badgers pinching his berries, had rigged up the net to keep the raiders away. But it took more than a net to stop Ben. With one twist of his powerful neck he pulled out a peg, then he started hauling at the mesh.

Released from the entangling net, the frightened fawn scrambled to its feet. Then the deer fled to the safety of the trees. Ben paid little attention. The strawberries were delicious.

And for nearly half an hour, Old Ben gorged himself on the berries. Then, when he could eat no more, he squirmed under a hole in the fence and headed for home.

After breakfast, Dave came out to look at his garden. What a shock he got. "That greedy old badger's been here again," he yelled. He took an angry kick at one of the uprooted stakes. "I should have used bigger ones," he muttered. Then he turned to his dog. "Come on, Sandy. You can pick up his trail. This time we're going to catch that old villain."

High above the cottage the trail led, through gullies, streams and woods, but Sandy, sniffing excitedly managed to stick to it.

Then at last they spotted Ben, ambling along a ledge. Sandy let out a triumphant bay. At once the old badger broke into a gallop.

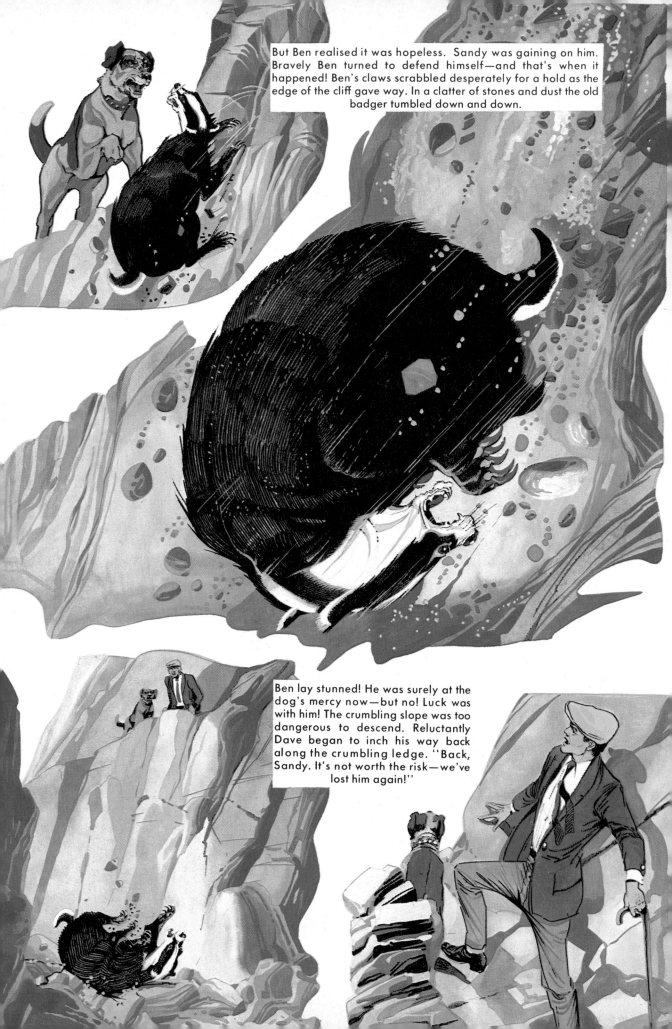

But Ben realised it was hopeless. Sandy was gaining on him. Bravely Ben turned to defend himself—and that's when it happened! Ben's claws scrabbled desperately for a hold as the edge of the cliff gave way. In a clatter of stones and dust the old badger tumbled down and down.

Ben lay stunned! He was surely at the dog's mercy now—but no! Luck was with him! The crumbling slope was too dangerous to descend. Reluctantly Dave began to inch his way back along the crumbling ledge. ''Back, Sandy. It's not worth the risk—we've lost him again!''

Ever so slowly, Ben recovered his reeling senses. Then he staggered along the trail for home.

And for the second time that day he crossed the path of his old enemy, Varga the wildcat. The cat quickly sensed that the limping badger was in trouble. Here was Varga's chance to get revenge. Fangs bared, he leaped on Ben.

The badger was in no shape for a fight. Ben's senses reeled as his enemy's teeth and claws flashed again and again . . .

Suddenly Ben heard pounding hooves. Then Varga, with a terrified screech, went flying head over heels. The father of the fawn Ben had freed from the strawberry net had arrived in the nick of time. A debt had been repaid!

As Varga limped off, Ben scurried off to his sett. There he licked his wounds and curled up for a quiet snooze. That feed of strawberries had brought him a lot of trouble, but it was just another day in the life of Old Ben, the badger.

GINGER

HOUSE-PROUD!

STRANGE HOMES OF THE ANIMAL WORLD

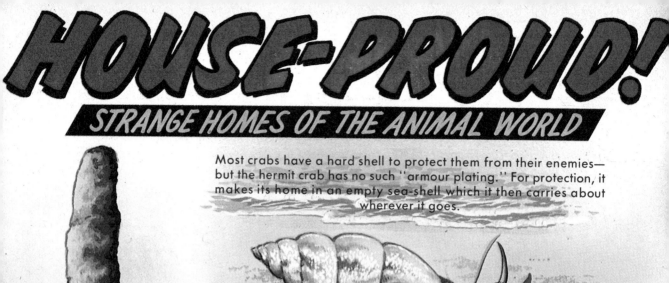

Most crabs have a hard shell to protect them from their enemies—but the hermit crab has no such "armour plating." For protection, it makes its home in an empty sea-shell which it then carries about wherever it goes.

Towers like this are the skyscrapers of the insect world! They are built by termites, and often house almost a million of the tiny ant-like creatures.

The red-necked grebe's home is always on the move! It cunningly builds a floating nest which can be mistaken for a clump of debris.

Even some fish build nests! The little sticklebacks of our ponds and streams build underwater nests of water weed, in which the female lays her eggs.

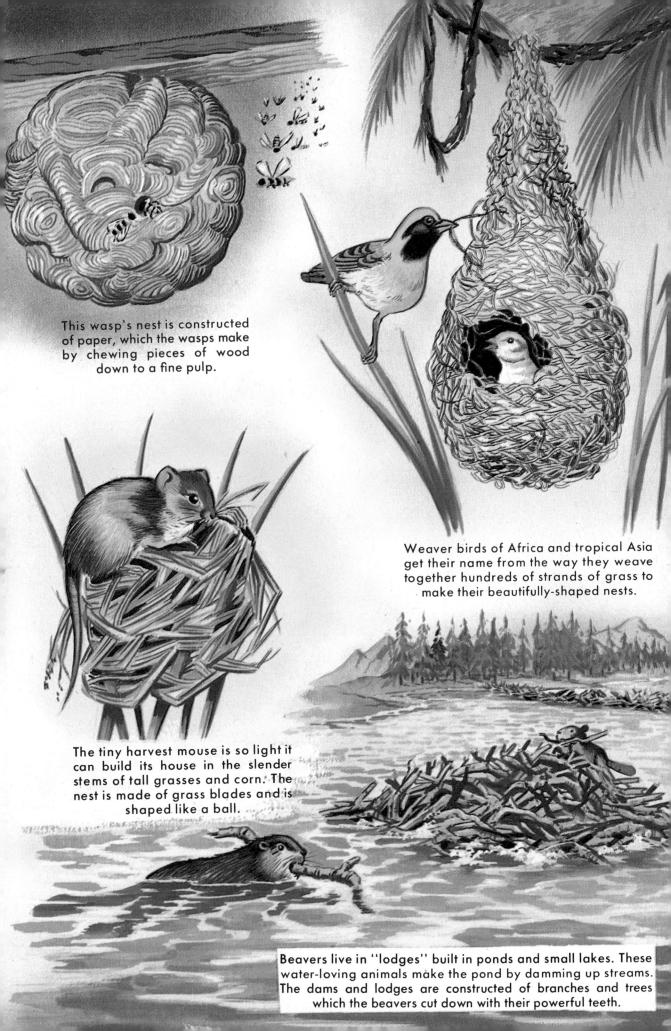

This wasp's nest is constructed of paper, which the wasps make by chewing pieces of wood down to a fine pulp.

Weaver birds of Africa and tropical Asia get their name from the way they weave together hundreds of strands of grass to make their beautifully-shaped nests.

The tiny harvest mouse is so light it can build its house in the slender stems of tall grasses and corn. The nest is made of grass blades and is shaped like a ball.

Beavers live in "lodges" built in ponds and small lakes. These water-loving animals make the pond by damming up streams. The dams and lodges are constructed of branches and trees which the beavers cut down with their powerful teeth.

IT'S A SUPER RAKE—AND NO MISTAKE!

HE'S NOT SO BLUE WHEN HE LEAVES THE ZOO.

Dicky Burd

THE FUN IS FINE WITH EACH ROAD SIGN.

The NUMSKULLS

DOES BLINKY KNOW HIS ROAD SIGNS? LOOK AT THE NEXT PAGE TO FIND OUT.

ROAD WORKS

BLINKY'S ANSWER—
"MAN HAVING TROUBLE OPENING HIS BROLLY"

ALL MOTOR VEHICLES PROHIBITED

BLINKY'S ANSWER—
"BEWARE OF LOW-FLYING MOTOR BIKES."

TWO WAY TRAFFIC CROSSES ONE-WAY ROAD

BLINKY'S ANSWER—
"TWO INDIANS HAVING A FIGHT."

CHILDREN

BLINKY'S ANSWER—
"TWO KIDS RUNNING TO BUY THEIR 'BEEZERS' BEFORE THEY'RE SOLD OUT."

UNEVEN ROAD

BLINKY'S ANSWER—
"BEWARE OF BOWLER HATS ON THE ROAD."

TWO WAY TRAFFIC STRAIGHT AHEAD

BLINKY'S ANSWER—
"SAME TWO INDIANS, BUT ONE HAS CHASED THE OTHER UP A CLIFF!"

NO CYCLING

BLINKY'S ANSWER—
"LOOK OUT FOR RIDERLESS BIKES."

STEEP HILL

BLINKY'S ANSWER—
"PYRAMIDS AHEAD!"

HO! HO! THE EXAMINER SAID MY ANSWERS WERE ALL WRONG. WE'LL HAVE TO GET BRAINY FIT BEFORE OUR NEXT TEST.

TEEZERS

Poor old Blinky! He thinks he knows the person in the picture, but there are really five "Beezer" characters there. See if you can identify them from the parts shown.

The potter who made this collection of vases added something extra to each new one he made. Can you work out what the fourth one should look like and complete the drawing?

Ginger won't get his electric kettle to boil until he finds the correct plug. Help him by tracing the cables to find which plug is fixed to the kettle.

Fatty's starving as usual, but the letters on the boxes have got mixed up. See if you can sort out the jumbled letters to make the names of five kinds of food.

ANSWERS

CARROT PUZZLE :—
Bun pinched 8 carrots on the first day, 14 on the second, 20 on the third, 26 on the fourth and 32 on the fifth.

FOOD NAMES:— Meat pies, Trifle, Chicken Sandwiches and Biscuits.

KETTLE PUZZLE:— Plug "C".   **NAME PICTURE:—** Ginger.

PICTURE:—
The parts in the puzzle are:—Black Bun's ears, Little Mo's head, Brainy's jacket and waistcoat, Blink's right leg, and Mr Flippy's left leg.

VASES:—
The fourth vase should be like this:—

DELIBERATE MISTAKES:—
(1) There is a fork instead of another sword behind the shield. (2) On the shield there is a sausage in place of a lion. (3) The pike that the knight is holding has a gap in the shaft. (4) There is a football boot on the knight's right foot. (5) The sign says "Admission Free" but shows the prices of admission below. (6) The wire for holding up the right-hand picture is below it instead of above. (7) There is a corkscrew on the end of Blink's umbrella. (8) Tiny's left hand has six fingers. (9) One of the pistols on the wall has the trigger on top. (10) Fingers' trousers.

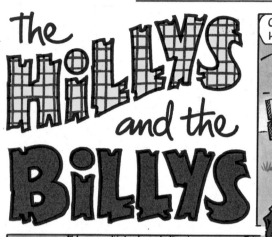

CRAZY

Almost a hundred years ago, a rich Frenchwoman left 125,000 francs to buy clothes—for snowmen!

No pistols or swords for two Munich butchers when they fought a duel. They battered each other with giant sausages!

In a sea battle last century, between two ships from Uruguay and Brazil, the Uruguayan ship ran out of ammunition—so it shelled the enemy ship with hard cheeses!

An American counted himself lucky when he fell from a 70-storey New York skyscraper! He landed on a lorryload of mattresses and escaped unhurt!

Stefan Rashenkov, of Warsaw, has something to "blow" about. He huffed and puffed a feather along for two miles!

CAPERS

The craze of pole-squatting swept through the U.S.A. some years ago. Maurie Kirby, of Indiana, stayed on top of a 71-foot high pole for 211 days.

PORT AUGUSTA 1100 MILES

BRISBANE 1100 MILES

2200 weary miles from Port Augusta to Brisbane and an Australian once pedalled all the way—on a child's tricycle!

Imagine teaching Redskins all about bows and arrows! That's what had to be done a year or two ago when some Crow Indians were hired as extras for a Western film! It turned out they'd never used them.

HE WANTS QUIET—NOT A RIOT!

BABY Crockett

NEXT MORNING, 6 AM —

I'm as quiet as a mouse today.

Oh, no! He tripped!

CRASH!

GRR!

I know what to do tonight.

Me stuff my ears with cotton wool.

WOOL

NEXT MORNING —

Get up, Baby! It's nearly twelve o'clock! You've overslept.

Oh! And me was to meet Willum at the boats at nine!

You're too late! All the boats are booked!

Sorry, Willum! I overslept! But I won't tomorrow.

NEXT MORNING —

Thanks for being so noisy. You wakened me up! I shan't be late today!

Eh?

WHAT A BLINKIN

LAUGH!

WHERE TO GO?—SOON THEY'LL KNOW!

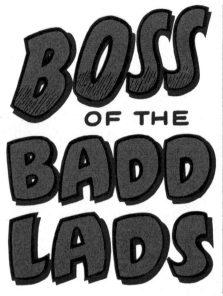

OUR SHERIFF'S AN APE!

THIEVING doesn't pay in the country near Coyote Creek. Clint Jackson found that out when he tried to pinch the gold nugget old Gabby Smith had mined. Clint was promptly arrested by the two sheriffs.

That's right—two sheriffs! Most towns have just one, but Coyote Creek has two. There's an ordinary guy, name of Danny Blain—and there's Charlie. He's the one who scares the livin' daylights outa rustlers, cattle thieves and bank robbers. No wonder! He's a six-foot-three, twenty-stone, educated ape wearin' a star!

SURE AM MIGHTY GRATEFUL TO CHARLIE FOR ALL HE DONE. GOT A LITTLE PRESENT FOR HIM ONCE HE'S LOCKED THAT GUY UP.

That little present from Gabby turned out to be a gold nugget bigger'n a rock bun!

HERE Y'ARE, CHARLIE.

Maybe Charlie thought it WAS a rock bun, 'cos he took a bite at it! Ouch! It was hard!

Charlie gave one almighty roar that sent Gabby Smith harin' for the hills. Then he drew back his arm. Danny leaped forward.

NO, CHARLIE! DON'T THROW IT AWAY.

Danny explained to his pal that gold nuggets are not for eatin'.

BANK

COME ON. THE BEST PLACE FOR THAT IS THE BANK.

No bank manager ever had a stranger signature on his files! No, sir!

But suddenly—

SHERIFF! THE STAGE HAS BEEN HELD UP!

The gang who'd held up the stage sure had made a thorough job of it—they'd even pinched the hosses!

Danny got the whole story from the driver.

THEY WENT FOR MAH GUARD, HERE, AND BEAT HIM UP.

THEY AIN'T GETTIN' AWAY WITH THIS!

EVERYBODY GET YOUR HOSSES. WE'RE GOIN' AFTER THE VARMINTS.

In a matter of minutes, Danny Blain was riding off with a posse. Every able-bodied guy in town joined him on the vengeance trail. Well — nearly everyone! The most able-bodied of them all didn't have a hoss! That was Charlie!

But Charlie wasn't gonna be left out if he could help it. He set off on a nag-hunt and mighty soon found one. An' what a nag! It shoulda been in a rest home—not on sale!

LUKE SHARPE HOSS TRADER

SORRY— NO PART EXCHANGE

EX RACE HOSS FOR SALE
GOOD RUNNER
WELL SHOD
CHEAP FOR QUICK SALE
OWNER EMIGRATIN'!

Charlie dumped its crooked owner in a water barrel and leaped on his hoss. WHUMP! Not surprisingly, it folded up.

HOSS TRADER

So Charlie hoisted it to its feet again. On the way up, though, its rump met a cactus.

Yahoo! Off it went like the winner o' the Kentucky Derby. Charlie only just made it on to its back.

He didn't stay on it long! He was so occupied hangin' on, he didn't see a low branch comin' up. KERRUNCH!

So there he was—only half a mile outa town and with no hoss. He sure was wild!

Stompin' back into town still gruntin' with rage, he spotted a real beauty of a hoss at the hitchin' rail outside the bank.

Charlie didn't know whose it was—and he didn't care. He needed it to join the posse, so he leaped into the saddle.

And could that hoss go! It nearly took the whiskers off old Ben Green as it streaked past him!

Only trouble was—it went in the opposite direction to the one Charlie wanted to go!

Up hills and down valleys Charlie was carried. His mount seemed to know where it was headin' . . .

. . . because, when it reached an old shack 'way up in the hills, it skidded to a halt. Charlie was sent flyin' into the horse trough.

Charlie was fed up. Soaking wet and saddle sore, the hairy sheriff staggered into the shack to rest his aching bones.

There was nobody at home, so Charlie plonked himself down on the bed in the back room and fell asleep.

He wouldn't have slept if he'd known what was goin' on back in Coyote Creek. Black Jake Ross was stickin' up the bank!

LOAD ALL YUH KIN GET INTO MAH BAG.

It was all too easy. The rest of Jake's gang had held up the coach to lure the sheriff and the posse out of town so that there would be nobody left to stop their boss.

Chuckling to himself, Jake left the bank. Suddenly his chuckle changed to a roar of anger.

SOME ROTTEN THIEF HAS PINCHED MAH HOSS!

He'd have to escape on foot! Jake wasn't used to runnin', and he was a-puffin' mighty hard by the time he reached the edge of town. Then—

A HOSS! IT'S A REAL BAG O' BONES, BUT IT'LL HAVE TO DO.

So, instead of a real excitin' dash to his hide out, Jake was carried into the hills by Charlie's old nag at a slow stagger. It didn't do his temper no good, either!

He was real mad by the time he met up with his gang.

WHAT KEPT YUH? WE BIN HERE FOR AGES.

SHURRUP! GIMME A HOSS.

Then the gang rode off to the hide-out. When they reached it, Jake's temper still hadn't improved.

PUT THE LOOT THAR—AN' BRING IN THE STUFF YOU STOLE FROM THE COACH! AH'LL DO THE SHARIN' OUT.

Jake's fierce voice put the fear o' death into his gang. But it did more than that. It carried through to the back room and woke Charlie. Yup! The hut Charlie had gone to sleep in was the gang's hide-out!

Charlie peeped out of the back room, and the first thing he saw was Jake holdin' up a gold nugget —Charlie's nugget.

LOOK AT THAT! WHAT A BEAUTY!

Next second, a tornado hit the gang. Leastways, that's what it musta seemed like. It was Charlie makin' sure no lout pinched HIS nugget. KRUNCH! One hairy fist landed on Jake's skull.

WHAM! Quick-draw Grogan and Lars the Swede were squashed against the wall before they could fire.

Gonzales tried to throw his knife. But instead HE was thrown —right through the window. The fact it was shut didn't bother Charlie—but it made things painful for Gonzales.

It was all over in seconds. Charlie lashed the desperadoes together on the two good horses. He was none too gentle, either.

ARGH! YOU'RE CUTTIN' ME IN HALF!

What a surprise the folk got when Charlie brought the gang back to Coyote Creek!

SHERIFF'S OFFICE AND JAIL

IT'S BLACK JAKE!

HOW DOES CHARLIE DO IT?

HEY! CHARLIE'S CAUGHT THE GANG WHO ROBBED THE STAGE!

The bank manager wasn't too surprised to give Charlie a nice reward, though!

And Danny Blain thought he knew the best place for Charlie's money.

BANK

COME ON, PAL. YOU CAN ADD THAT TO YOUR BANK ACCOUNT.

But Charlie didn't agree!

Banks didn't seem the safest place for money —not while there were folks like Black Jake Ross and his gang around. So Charlie put his money and his nugget into a big tin.

YOUR MONEY AIN'T GONNA BE VERY SAFE THERE, CHARLIE.

Wasn't it! Charlie didn't let the tin out of his sight all day. When night came he put it under his pillow and fixed it to his own alarm system—a string, with lots of bells on it, tied to the trigger of a six-shooter. That, Charlie reckoned, was safer than puttin' it in a bank.

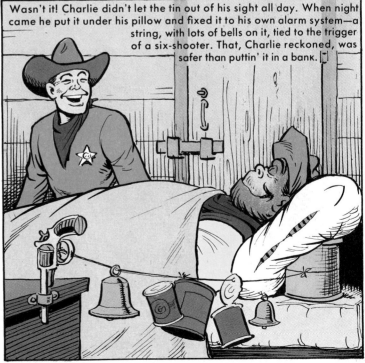

POP DICK AND HARRY

POP HAS SECOND THOUGHTS ABOUT THOSE HOLIDAY SPOTS!